Contents

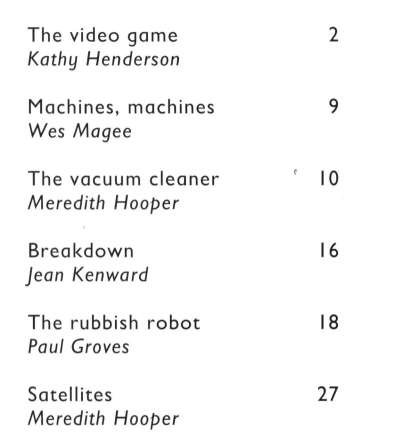

The video game

Susie had a video game. She pressed the start
button. A little man came on to the screen.
He waved. Susie pressed the A button and the little
man jumped. She pressed the B button and he ran.
Susie pressed all the buttons.

She pressed them again and again and the little
man ran and jumped. He went up a mountain and
went swinging through the trees.

Then, suddenly, he fell down into a cave where there were lots of monsters.

"Help!" said a voice.

Susie looked round. There was nobody there.

"Help me, Susie!" said the voice again.

Susie looked back at the screen. The voice was coming from the little man.

"Get me out of here!" he cried. "Please get me out of here!"

Susie pressed the buttons but the monsters were still there. She pressed them again but she couldn't make them go away.

Suddenly she stopped.

"How can you talk?" she said to the little man. "You are just a video game!"

"Help!" he cried. "Please help or the monsters will eat me up!"

"If they eat you up, you can always have another life in a video game," said Susie.

"No!" said the little man. "I have got one life just like you. Help! Help!"

Susie pressed the buttons again but the monsters were still there. They looked very hungry.

"Oh dear! I don't know how to help you!" said Susie. "I have pressed all the buttons but they don't work!"

She stopped and thought. "Perhaps if I switch the game off the monsters will go away." Susie pressed the OFF button but the monsters were still there.

"Help!" cried the little man again. Susie turned the video game machine over and took out the batteries.

When she looked at the screen

again the monsters were still there.

"Quick!" cried the little man.

"How can I help you? Tell me how to help you!"

cried Susie.

"Just give me your hand," said the little man.

Susie put out her hand and touched the screen.

Suddenly, there was the little man in her hand.

He was very small.

"Oh, thank you, Susie," he said. "You have saved

my life!" Susie smiled.

Just then there was a big bang from the video game machine. Susie looked at the screen. It had gone grey.

"Look!" she said to the little man. "The monsters have gone." But when she looked down, her hand was empty.

Machines, machines

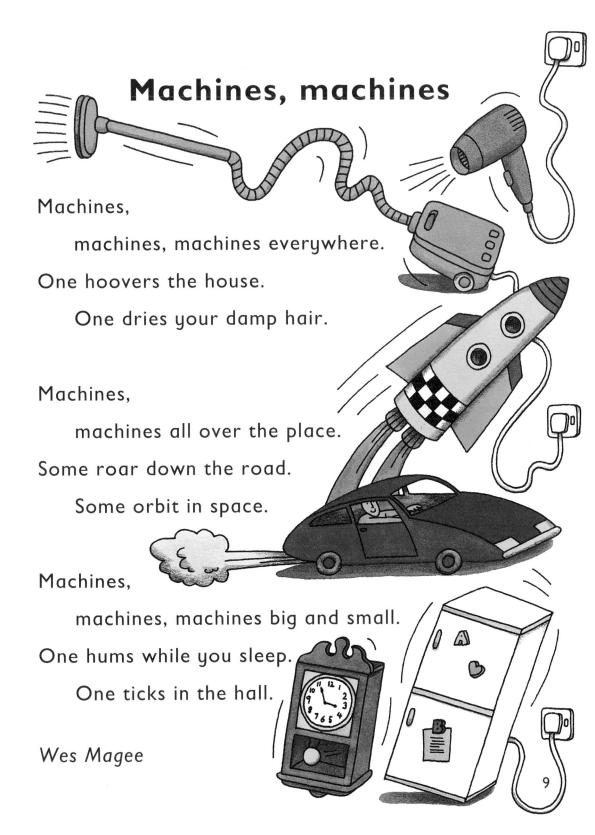

Machines,

    machines, machines everywhere.

One hoovers the house.

    One dries your damp hair.

Machines,

    machines all over the place.

Some roar down the road.

    Some orbit in space.

Machines,

    machines, machines big and small.

One hums while you sleep.

    One ticks in the hall.

Wes Magee

The vacuum cleaner

Cleaning can be hard work, but there are machines to help us with some things. Before there were any machines, cleaning was very, very hard work. Dust got into carpets and curtains and chairs. Dirt stuck to everything. Lots of people had to work all day to clean a big house, so many inventors were trying to make a machine which would do the cleaning for them.

Manual vacuum cleaner 1903

One day, a man called Mr Booth went to see a new cleaning machine in London.

"Look at this," said the inventor of the new machine. "My cleaning machine will take all the dust out of a carpet."

The machine blew air down into the carpet. This made the dust blow up in clouds. Then most of the dust fell back on the carpet.

Mr Booth looked at the new cleaning machine.

"I have a better idea," he said. "I won't blow the dust away. I'll try to suck the dust out."

Then he sucked the back of his chair to see if his idea would work. The dust came flying out!

Mr Booth coughed and coughed.

Mr Booth invented a big machine to suck up dust. He called his machine a vacuum cleaner.

Booth's vacuum cleaner, 1905

The vacuum cleaner was pulled along the street by a horse. A very long pipe went from the machine through a window into a house. The vacuum cleaner sucked up dust out of the carpet and curtains through the pipe. It sucked up dirt from the chairs, but it made lots of noise. People were frightened. Horses ran away.

Mr Booth invented a clear pipe so people could see the dust and dirt going out of their houses. Even the King and Queen asked Mr Booth to take his vacuum cleaner to Buckingham Palace.

In America a poor inventor thought of a new idea. He invented a small vacuum cleaner. His machine had a brush to help get out the dirt. It had a dust bag and a handle. The inventor was so poor that he made the dust bag from an old pillow case and the handle from an old broom.

Hoover advertisement 1931

A man called Mr Hoover lived near by. He made things for horses. The car had just been invented, and people didn't need lots of things for horses any more, so Mr Hoover wanted to find something new to make. He bought the idea of the small vacuum cleaner from the poor inventor.

Soon Mr Hoover made lots of vacuum cleaners for people to have in their houses. Now people could have a vacuum cleaner of their own.

Breakdown

Rackerty clackerty
 clickerty BONG
the washing machine
 has gone terribly wrong,

It's swallowed a button!
 It's stuck in its jaw!
Do you think it will ever
 get out any more?

Hark at it spluttering
 clickerty-bump —
the washing is churning
 all up in a lump.

And just for a button
　　　so shiny and small!
O why did we ever
　　　have buttons at all?

Rackerty clackerty
　　　clickerty clack...
Hooray! THAT sounds better –
　　　the button's come back!

Jean Kenward

The rubbish robot

Penny and Peter were on their way to school one day when they heard a funny noise. It came from under some old bottles and boxes on the path. They went to see what it was. They had a surprise. It was a robot! It was crying.

"What is it?" asked Penny. "Why are you crying?"

"I'm a rubbish robot,"

said the robot. "I'm rubbish!

I'm rubbish! I'm rubbish!"

"Why?" asked Peter.

"I can't count."

"A robot that can't count," laughed Penny.

"You see, you laughed at me," said the robot.

"No, we didn't," said Peter. He was cross with

Penny. "What's your name?" he asked.

"Rupert," said the robot.

"You must come to school with us, Rupert, and learn to count," said Penny.

"I'm a rubbish robot. I can't learn in school. I'm rubbish."

"Do come with us. Mrs Ball will help you," said Peter. "How can you learn if you won't try?"

"Yes. You are right," said Rupert. "I **will** go to school with you and I'll try."

The robot walked to school with Penny and Peter. He walked very slowly so they were all late.

"Where have you been?" asked Mrs Ball.

"We found this robot," said Penny. "He made us late. He's called Rupert. He can't count."
Mrs Ball laughed.

"You see," said Rupert. "You laughed at me."

"No, I laughed because of the fun we can have," said Mrs Ball. "Just press your tummy buttons. Look: 1, 2, 3, 4, 5, 6, 7, 8, 9, 10."

Rupert tried. "0, 1, 0, 1, 0, 1, 0, 1, 0, 1.

You see, I can't do it. I'm rubbish."

"No, you are not!" said Mrs Ball. "I'll tell you a

counting rhyme.

1, 2, robot stew.

3, 4, chips galore.

5, 6, add oil and mix.

7, 8, bolts on a plate.

9, 10, count again.

Now you try."

Rupert laughed for the first time that morning.

"Press your tummy buttons as you say it," said Mrs Ball.

"1, 2, robot stew," said Rupert.

"3, 4, chips galore.

5, 6, add oil and mix.

7, 8, bolts on a plate.

9, 10, count again.

I can do it! I can do it! I can count! I'm not a rubbish robot!" shouted Rupert. "Can I come to your school? I'll be your robot."

"Yes," said Mrs Ball. "A robot would be a good thing to have at school. But where do you come from?"

"I don't know where my home is. I'm lost," said Rupert.

"He can live with us," shouted Peter.

Just then a man came in.

"What are you doing with my robot?" he asked.

"We found him under some boxes," said Peter.

"In the street," said Penny.

"Mrs Ball has helped me to count," said Rupert. "I'm not a rubbish robot now."

"Oh, but you **are** a rubbish robot," said the man, "and a very good one. Rupert sorts out the rubbish in my recycling factory."

"Can't he come to school?" asked Penny. "We like him!"

"No, I need him at work," said the man.

"Please?" said Rupert. "I want to learn some more things at school."

"Oh, please!" shouted all the children.

The man laughed. "Well, all right. He can come just in the morning, then," he said.

All the children shouted:

"1, 2, robot stew.

3, 4, chips galore.

5, 6, add oil and mix.

7, 8, bolts on a plate.

9, 10, count again."

Satellites

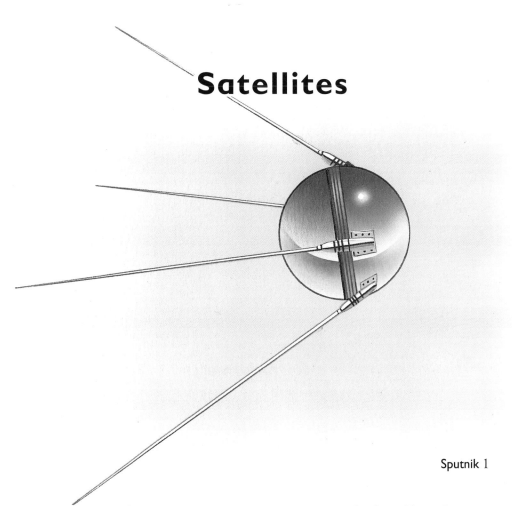

Sputnik 1

Sputnik 1 started whizzing round the Earth in 1957. It was the first satellite made by people. Sputnik 1 was a little ball with a radio. It was just as big as a football, but it looked as bright as a star as it whizzed across the night sky.

Now there are lots of big satellites orbiting the Earth.

Tracking and data relay satellite

Satellites tell us about the Earth, from the outside. They send us news and messages all day and all night. They are like eyes and ears that never sleep.

Some satellites stay near to Earth. Some satellites are a long way out in space, 36 thousand kilometres from Earth.

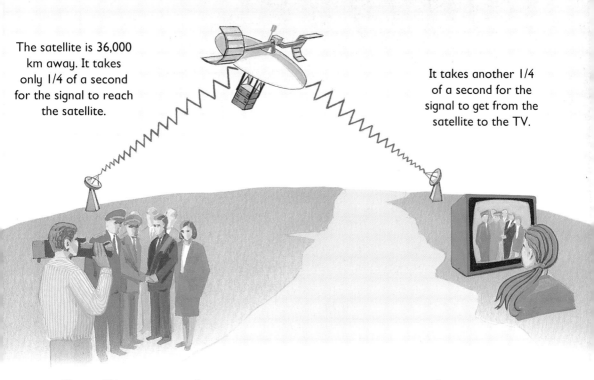

The satellite is 36,000 km away. It takes only 1/4 of a second for the signal to reach the satellite.

It takes another 1/4 of a second for the signal to get from the satellite to the TV.

Satellites can let us see news on our television screens from anywhere in the world, very quickly. A television signal goes all the way out to the satellite, 36 thousand kilometres away, in a quarter of a second. The satellite sends the message down to our television set in the next quarter of a second, and we see the picture on the television screen.

If there is something in the way, the message will not get through. Even the leaves of a tree will stop the picture.

Communications satellite

Some satellites carry our telephone calls across the world. Other satellites take pictures to help us find out things about the world. The pictures can tell us about the weather and where there are fish in the sea and where there is dirt in the rivers and factory smoke in the air.

Some satellites do not look at the Earth. They look the other way, out into space, and tell us about the stars.

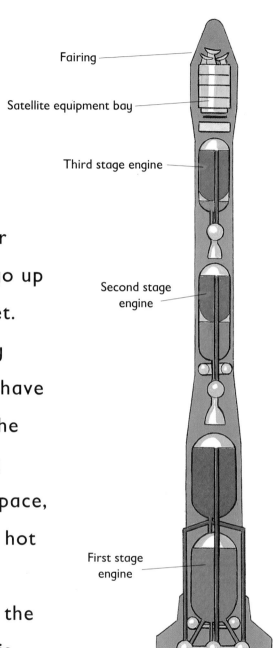

Fairing

Satellite equipment bay

Third stage engine

Second stage engine

First stage engine

Viking 5 engines

Satellites and their special instruments go up into space in a rocket. They have to be very strong because they have a long, hard trip in the rocket and then they have to work up in space, where it can be very hot or cold.

This satellite is at the top of the rocket. It is two times taller than a man.

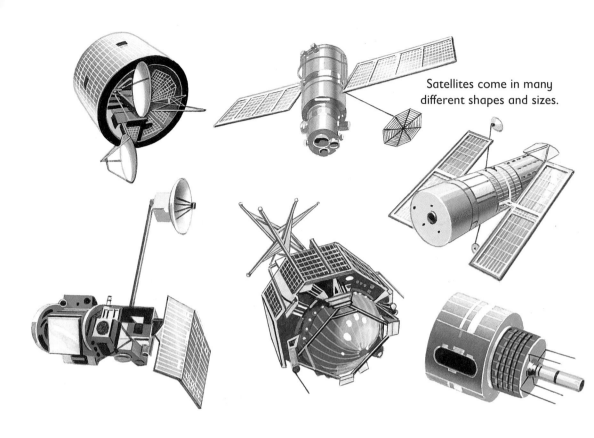

Satellites come in many different shapes and sizes.

Satellites have little gas jets to help them get into the right place above the Earth. When the satellites get old, new satellites take their place.

But the old satellites do not go away. They keep on orbiting the Earth. Even if they fall to bits, the bits keep on orbiting. Now there is lots of rubbish orbiting round the Earth in space. Space rubbish is a big new problem.